Contents

This edition first published in the UK in 2010
By Green Umbrella Publishing

© Green Umbrella Publishing 2010
www.gupublishing.co.uk

Publisher: Vanessa Gardner

Printed and bound in the UK

ISBN: 978-1-907311-77-2

Creative Director: Kevin Gardner

Written and edited by Michael Lee

Images courtesy of Getty and Shutterstock

Introduction

In this bookazine I will enlarge on the lives and careers of three of the famous men of steam. I have defined their qualities roughly as follows: George Stephenson can be called a visionary and the prophet of the steam railway system. Samuel Smiles, who wrote the contemporaneous account of George Stephenson's life, is his St Paul. George could do no wrong in his eyes. Robert Stephenson excelled as an accomplished chief of staff, motivating and freely acknowledging the input of those who worked for him. Isambard Kingdom Brunel created a railway of heroic proportions stamping it with a style that forever made the Great Western different to all others. He was no locomotive engineer, however, but his enthusiasm for the propulsion of large ships by steam power enables me to include him among the heroes of steam.

The accounts that follow are old and familiar stories to students of railway history. It is important to remind ourselves how very different the world was when these men were creating the railway system that our modern trains still use. The following accounts will illustrate what I mean. For instance, in 1832, George Stephenson was heavily criticised for bringing in his own men instead of using local workmen. Traditionally, the stagecoach proprietors would recruit stagecoach drivers from men that were local to each stretch of the road between towns and villages. They would best know the road and

Robert Stephenson (left) and George Stephenson.

how to manage the horses over it.

Stephenson was creating his new iron road by the labour of outsiders, itinerant gangs of navvies who had expertise in the building of cuttings, tunnels and embankments because of their experience in canal building. None but the men of Northumberland had any knowledge of the management of his iron horses. So it was the Geordies from the pit railways that were recruited to be the first locomotive drivers, shedmasters and firemen. It was a monopoly, but it was the result of the paucity of experience in this field.

And again, when we casually read that Robert Stephenson and Co. built a locomotive and delivered it to work on such and such railway, we should contemplate the fact that the boiler and wheels were lifted onto a horse-drawn lorry which took them to a wharf, where they were placed on the deck of a wooden sailing vessel that then carried them to Liverpool (or Maidenhead, in the case of North Star) to be put on rails for the first time when the tracks had reached the point of disembarkation.

We should also think of the extreme youth of men like Daniel Gooch, locomotive superintendent of the Great Western at twenty-one. Having designed some efficient and speedy engines for his railway, he often drove them himself. When the Great Western first reached Exeter, Gooch drove a special train which left London at 07.30 a.m. and was hauled by Aetaeon a loco with seven

foot driving wheels. The train reached Exeter (194 miles) at 12.30 p.m. After attending a celebratory dinner, Gooch was back at the controls of his engine, setting off again at 5.20 p.m. He reached Paddington at 10.00 p.m. Gooch had driven 387 miles, had been at the engine shed long before 07.00 a.m., had only sat down at the dinner and had probably drunk several toasts to the success of the line before driving the return journey. It was almost certainly a 19-hour day, with 18 of them on his feet. For this reason enclosed cabs were not thought a wise option even by the regular drivers who feared that comfort would induce drowsiness.

The young Gooch was driving over newly created lines. No-one "knew the road", as we twentieth century drivers did having observed or fired scores of times over a route before signing for it. We see the result of this, on 30th September 1852. Gooch was at the controls of Lord of the Isles on the directors' special from London to Birmingham. The train was made up of 10 coaches, only one of which had a brake (and a guard), and this was next to the engine. The 120 mile run was to take two and three quarter hours. None of the men on Lord of the Isles knew the road. At Aynho they saw a stop signal at danger, thought it was a distant or warning signal and drove past it. Before they could stop they ran into the back of a mixed goods and passenger train that was shunting in the station! Luckily the driver of the mixed train, having detected the sound of wheels on the line behind him, hastily put on steam to get away from the approaching train. The sudden jerk that was the result broke a coupling on his train and some coaches and wagons were left behind, into which the special smashed. Lord of the Isles was derailed, wagons and coaches splintered and some platform stone work was torn up.

The other driver's alert action had prevented serious injuries to passengers and crew, but the board of trade was critical of everyone. Trains did not get failsafe continuous brakes for another twenty-three years.

Finally, to put us all firmly into that young and carefree age of the new iron road, when North Star ran the first train from Paddington to Maidenhead in June 1838, the return trip, after a celebratory dinner, was proceeding at an average speed of thirty miles per hour when Bristol director, T R Guppy, walked the full length of the train on the tops of the carriages. This was the world in which the heroics of George, Robert and Isambard were displayed. Times are very different today, though young men are still as daft.

George Stephenson's locomotive 'Rocket' comes in first at the trials competition held at Rainhill Bridge, 1829.

George Stephenson
VISIONARY

George Stephenson was born on 9th June 1781 in the lower room at the west end of a four-roomed house situated a hundred yards from Wylam, a colliery village on the north bank of the Tyne. He was the second of six children. The house stood by the side of the old post road between Hexham and Newcastle, and was divided so that four families had one room each. The rooms had bare rafters above, unplastered walls and clay floors at ground level. A wooden tramway along which chaldrons were hauled by horses ran in front of the house, and young children had to be watched lest they were run over.

George's father, Robert, was of Scottish descent. He had been living at Walbottle while working as a labourer at Wylam colliery, but when he met and married Mabel Carr and was made fireman of the old pumping engine that served the mine, he had moved to the house at Wylam. 'Old Bob' was a friendly man and 'Bob's Engine Fire' was a place where village children gathered to hear the stories that he told and to watch the wild birds that also found him hospitable. Robins hopped at his feet for a crumb or two, and George grew up with a similar affection for birds.

Eight years later, when the coal ran out, George's

The house where George Stephenson was born.

Civil engineer George
Stephenson.

father found a job at Dewly Burn colliery, and the family moved to a one-roomed cottage by a stream next to the mine. The young George earned a few pennies to help the family finances by watching over Widow Ainslie's cows that grazed along the wagon ways. Using clay from Dewly bog, he and a pal, Bill Thirlwall, made model engines using twine and corks to make the 'pit machinery'. Both of them were future engineers, Bill later became the engineer at a

mine near Alnwick. As George grew older he also earned pennies for leading ploughing horses, but he was always keen to work at the colliery. He started by picking slate out of the coal and later progressed to management of the gin horse that wound the haulage rope at the mineshaft. In time he became his father's assistant, firing the engine at Dewly. He was fourteen and earned a shilling a day. When the coal ran out again the family moved home, settling in another

Before the advent of the steam engine, coal was brought out of the mines by men and horses.

one-roomed cottage in Jolly's Close near Newburn. When the Newburn mine was enlarged, George became a fireman himself at the age of fifteen, working twelve hour shifts for two years sharing the duties with a lad named Coe. Now George's ambition was to be an engineman, and to that end he studied his engine so that when another new pit opened at Water Row, between the Wylam wagon way and the river Tyne, he joined his fireman father, and at the age of

seventeen he took the job of engineman or 'plugman'. He was now paid more than 'Old Bob' and was responsible for the proper working of the engine as it drew water up from the mine workings. When the water level fell suction holes were exposed preventing the pump from 'drawing'. These holes had to be plugged by the 'plugman' so that suction could recommence. As engineer he was required to call on the chief engineer in cases of the machinery

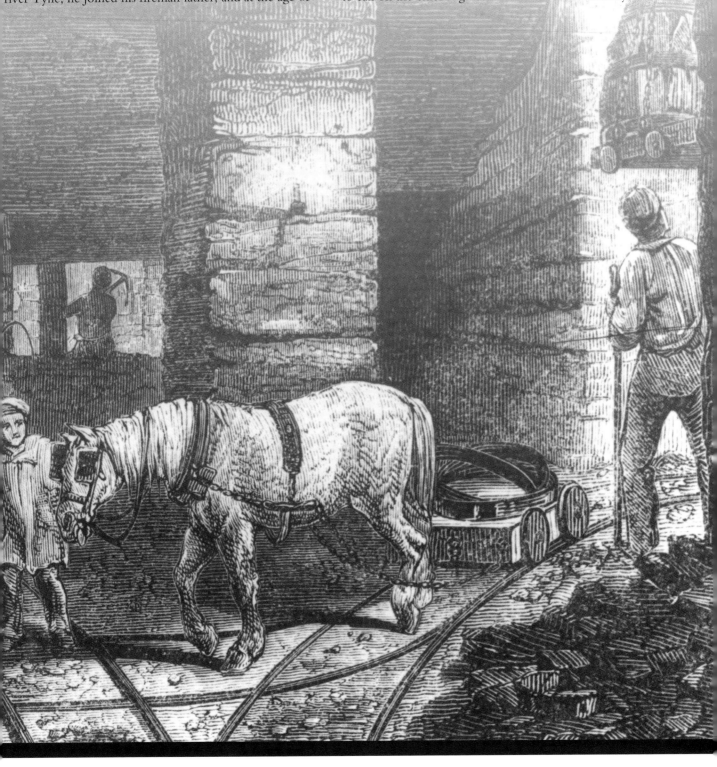

malfunctioning, but as a result of his genuine interest in the engine he gained a good understanding of its parts and he was able to fix most breakdowns himself.

The working of a Newcomen engine was accompanied by an extraordinary amount of wheezing, sighing, creaking and bumping. When the pump descended there was heard a plunge, a heavy sigh, and a loud bump. As the pump rose and the suction took effect there was a creak, a wheeze, another bump and a rush of water as it was lifted and poured out. We can picture the eighteen year old at the place of his work watching the swift glide and swing of the huge pumping engine. Every click and thump told a story, and the sudden rush of water as it welled up spoke of the hundred thousand gallons pumped during each twelve hour shift.

George could not yet read, but he was of a steady and thoughtful nature and if he could get someone to read an old newspaper to him he learned of the exploits of Bonaparte, then at large with his armies in Europe. From time to time information on the wonderful engines made by Boulton and Watt would form a short item of news, and he realised that only by 'learning his letters' would he be able to improve his knowledge.

As a grown man he had the courage to attend classes in the village with the sons of colliers and labourers, three evenings a week for threepence, paid to a poor schoolteacher named Robin Cowens. In 1799 he attended Andrew Robertson's arithmetic classes in Newburn for fourpence a week, doing his homework while attending to his pumping engine at the colliery.

At Water Row he learned the art of braking an engine. This was a well paid job, and it was thanks to his pal Coe that he was given the chance to acquire the skill. Subsequently he was given the brakesman's job at Black Callertons Dolly Pit in 1801 at the age of twenty. He now lived in the house of a local farmer and became the admirer of Fanny Henderson, a servant at the house. Fanny was comely, sweet tempered, modest and sensible, and

The Boulton & Watt Soho Manufactory near Birmingham where steam engines were built.

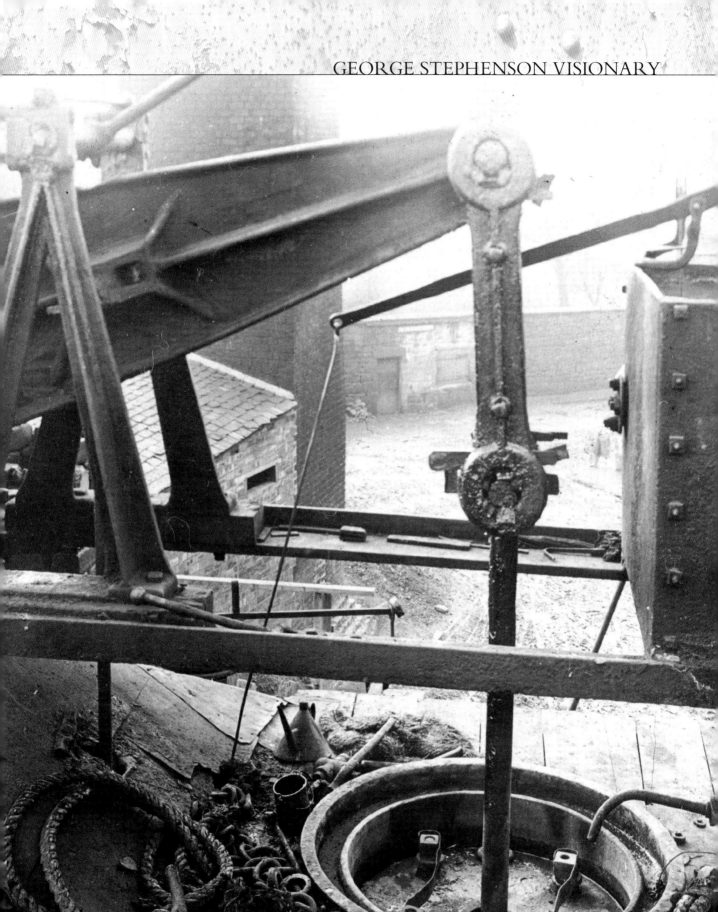

The wheezing and creaking Newcomen engine at Farme Colliery, Rutherglen.

George, who now mended shoes to add to his income, was delighted to have her small footwear to work on from time to time during the nightshifts at the colliery when there was less for him to do.

Some months later he was offered the brakesman's job at Willington Ballast Hill for higher pay. This encouraged him to set up home with Fanny in a rented cottage at Willington Quay. With the help of Fanny's savings added to his own he furnished the cottage, and in November 1802 they were married in Newburn church. Their cottage was one of several that lined the riverside, behind which was a huge hill of ballast taken from the holds of ships about to be loaded with coal. George was to be brakesman of the stationary engine that hauled the wagons of ballast to the summit of the great pile. As a result of his studies, George was able to sign his name in the church register. After the ceremony the couple visited the home of George's parents,

'Old Bob' was still a fireman but was becoming infirm. Then, while seated on a farm horse with Fanny behind him and her arms around his waist, they rode the fifteen miles to their cottage. The bridesman and bridesmaid, similarly mounted on a second horse, accompanied them.

George still used his spare time to add to his savings. He worked at shovelling ballast out of the ships' holds and made and repaired shoes. After a chimney fire that sooted up their prized eight day clock, he cleaned and repaired it so successfully that he also became the local repairer of clocks and watches. It was at Willington Quay that George's only

George Stephenson

Frances Henderson

son, Robert, was born on 18th October 1803.

Towards the end of 1804, George was persuaded to take the job of brakesman at the West Moor Colliery at Killingworth, which had vast coal reserves and employed large numbers of people. The move was shortly marked by tragedy when Fanny died of consumption, leaving George with his baby son. While grieving for his lost companion he was asked to superintend the working of one of Boulton and Watt's engines at a large spinning works at Montrose in Scotland.

He left Robert in the care of his sister, Elender, and, with his kit on his back, walked the two hundred miles to Montrose. Stephenson stayed in Scotland for about twelve

the sump at the lower end of the pump. The water then spilled into the sump leaving the sand behind. His return to Killingworth was again made on foot.

During his absence George's father had been scalded in the face and blinded by an accident at the engine house. George used fifteen pounds of his savings to settle his father's debts, and he arranged for his parents to move to a cottage at Killingworth, where he supported them for many years. Although Stephenson was again employed as a brakesman, this was a low point in his life. England was at war, taxes were high, trade was bad and men were being pressed into serving the Navy or militia. In order to avoid military service George spent the remainder of his savings,

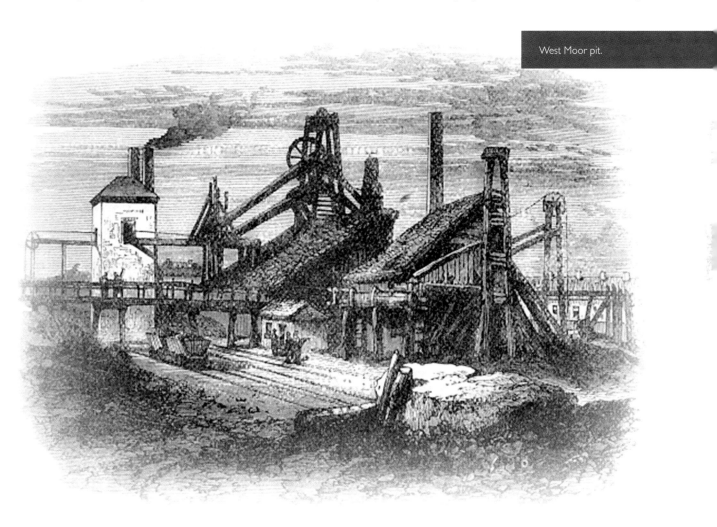

West Moor pit.

months and was paid enough to enable him to save twenty-eight pounds. During his time at Montrose he solved the problem of excessive wear on the bore and leathers of the pumping engine that he was responsible for. The wear was caused by sand carried in the water flow. George's solution was a twelve foot deep wooden 'boot' that he placed in

plus six pounds that he borrowed, to pay for a man to serve in his place. He was too poor at this stage to emigrate to America as his sister, Anne, and her husband had done.

His fortunes began to improve again in 1808 when he was contracted to be one of three enginemen supervising two engines at the West Moor pit. The engines worked night and day and two of the three enginemen were on duty at any time, each of them earning about twenty shillings per week. George made some alterations to the winding gear which increased the life of the haulage ropes. His habitual regular examination and maintenance of his engine and the knowledge that he acquired of the function of each part, gave him the chance to make a name for himself as a 'fixer of sick engines'. In 1810 the Newcomen engine at the newly opened Killingworth High pit failed to reduce water levels even after twelve months of pumping. Stephenson had not been impressed by the design of the engine when he had watched it being erected, and as the months passed and still the mine was unworkable he put his mind to the problem. After a thorough investigation of the engine he offered to make it work in a week. After having been given permission to try his hand, George did as he had promised. Choosing his own workmen he took the engine apart. He enlarged the water injection cock and ensured that it shut quickly and completely when the piston stroke began. He also raised the water cistern by ten feet and increased the boiler pressure from 5 lbs to 10 lbs. These alterations took three days to complete. Then, in front of a large crowd of observers, the engine was started with a series of exuberant bangs which caused some alarm. Once under load, however, the engine settled down and began to lift water. At ten o'clock that night the water in the pit had begun to fall, and by the next afternoon the workmen were able to descend to the bottom of the shaft. As a result of this achievement George was appointed engineman at the Killingworth High pit at a good wage, plus a payment of ten pounds for repairing the engine. By 1812 he was engine wright at the pit with a salary of one hundred pounds per year, and a horse to ride while making colliery inspections.

Stephenson continued to educate himself. He had a

One of Stephenson's achievements still in use, the power wheel used to drive a lathe at Killingworth Colliery, Northumberland.

friend by the name of John Wigham who was a farmer's son, and who gave him instruction in mathematics. He would set problems on George's slate for him to work on during his shifts. Wigham also taught George to draw plans and sections. When George became a famous man he remained grateful to the farmer's son who had helped him in his efforts to gain knowledge.

His own son, Robert, now nine years old, was a bright lad and was interested in the engines that George managed. For his part, George was determined that Robert would not have to face life unable to read or understand the use and rules of mathematics. In his spare time George made extra money from clock repairing and shoe making. He also devised patterns that enabled women to cut out and

Richard Trevithick.

make their own clothes. He used this extra income to send Robert to school at Long Benton then, when the boy was twelve, to a school in Newcastle. He bought the boy a donkey on which he would ride to and from school, wearing a grey suit that George had cut out and made, and with his books and food for the day on his back.

At home George taught his son how to read a plan of a machine without having to rely on textual information to describe the machine's action. At the pit, George set up engines above and below ground thus reducing the number of horses working underground from a hundred to fifteen. The time was approaching when George would apply his skills to locomotive construction. The old wooden wagon way that had been laid between Wylam and Lemington village had been replaced in 1808 by a plateway of cast iron enabling a single horse to draw up to three full wagons. In 1812 a rack had been laid along the plateway allowing Blackett's second primitive combination of Trevithick's and Blenkinsop's designs of travelling engine to be tried out. The maker, Tommy Waters of Gateshead, on finding it would not move, held down the safety valve and declared that: "Either he or she would go." The engine moved briefly before it 'flew all to pieces', Tommy was fortunate to survive. A third engine, also with rack drive, proved to be more successful and could pull eight or nine loaded wagons - when it did not jump off the rack.

Later the rack was taken away and William Hedley's smooth tyred engine appeared on the plateway after it had been re-laid with heavier rails. Stephenson went to see the engine that was working daily to and fro past the cottage in which he had been born, and came to the conclusion that he could make an engine that would work more steadily and efficiently. In 1813 George suggested to Lord Ravensworth, principal partner of the lessees of Killingworth colliery, that he might construct a travelling engine to haul coal from the mine to the river.

George was given permission and funds by Lord Ravensworth, whom some called a fool for advancing

George Stephenson and his son Robert at work together in their cottage.

The 'Blucher', George Stephenson's first successful locomotive.

money for such a project. It took ten months to build the engine which ran for the first time on 25th July 1814. It could haul eight loaded wagons totalling thirty tons up a slight gradient at four miles an hour. It closely resembled the Blenkinsop locomotive except that spur wheels driven by two cylinders engaged with gearing that turned smooth tyred wheels along the rail head. A chamber around the chimney preheated the water that was delivered to the boiler by a feed pump. The engine had no springs, but an attempt was made to equalise the weight between the boiler unit and the coal and water carrier by a lever connection.

It took a lot of effort to create this cumbersome and clumsy machine. George had to instruct the workmen and sort out initial problems with John Thirlwall, who was the blacksmith at West Moor. The spur gears did not provide a smooth drive and soon the teeth became worn and jerky in operation. At the end of twelve months the engine proved to be no more economical than horse power had been.

George saw that the major problem was the use of spur gearing. The following year he took out a patent, dated 28th February 1815, for an engine with direct drive from the pistons to the wheels. He used a ball and socket joint at the crossheads and crankpins to allow for uneven track causing a varied lift to the axles. At first the driving wheel sets were united by rods that joined cranks fitted to the axles at right angles to each other, but the cranks fractured in use. He then resorted to a chain running around indented wheels on the axles, so that the wheels turned in unison and maintained the right angle setting of the driven cranks, one to the other.

Eventually he hit upon a better method. The wheels on each side were kept in unison by rods on the outside of the wheel, so there was no need for a cranked axle. Direct connection to the crankpins was the elegant solution, and one still used on modern locomotives. Exhaust steam from the cylinders was turned into the chimney to speed up the rising action of the smoke. The coke fires burned more brightly as a result.

There was one more innovation that George tried on his improved engine in 1816. The light plateway responded badly to the increased weight and traffic, the rail joints became uneven so that derailments and slipping occurred too often, and at that time Stephenson was unable to get springs made that would support the heavy weight of the engine. His solution was to build four small cylinders into the lower part of the boiler, the pistons of which bore on

'Invicta', built for the Canterbury and Whitstable Railway, Kent.

Sir Humphry Davy, generally credited with the invention of the miner's safety lamp.

the axles. Boiler steam on the upper side of the pistons enabled each piston to take a quarter of the weight of the engine. The weight was then equal on each wheel despite changes in rail level. He also improved the design of the chairs that supported the track so that the rail ends met on more level terms.

It was about this time that George was risking his life in gas filled mine workings to test a safety lamp that he had invented. Explosive gases came out of the coal seams and miners using candles to see their way were often killed in underground explosions. The lamp that Stephenson developed became known as the 'Geordie Lamp' and though Stephenson did not fully understand the 'science' of what he had made, he knew that it was 'safe' when he himself took it into explosive gases. Sir Humphry Davy is famous for his safety lamp which he developed in accordance with scientific principles that he knew and understood. The coal owners presented Sir Humphry Davy with £2000, and Stephenson was given a hundred guineas. A certain amount of argument relating to the priority of their concepts was inevitable. Stephenson's supporters raised a further £1000 for George.

Locomotive building continued when Stephenson was asked to make a steam operated line between Hetton colliery in Durham and the coal shipment wharf on the river Wear, near Sunderland. The line was to be eight miles long and, because of the steepness of the gradients en route, there were five self acting inclines (i.e. full wagons going down hauling empty wagons going up) and two inclines with fixed engines hauling wagons by rope. Five of Stephenson's iron horses worked the remainder.

The railway opened on 18th November 1822 with George's brother, Robert, acting as resident engineer.

George's son, Robert, had left his Newcastle school in 1819 and was apprenticed to the head viewer at Killingworth for three years, after which George paid for him to attend Edinburgh University from October to the following summer. The six months cost George £80.00. He was now a married man again as in 1820, after many years alone, he wedded Elizabeth Hindmarsh, a farmer's daughter from Black Callerton.

Although George's engines continued to work their regular duties over several colliery lines year on year, the general public had yet to learn the potential value of rail transport. In the south of England, investors had lost money when the first public railway had been laid between the

A miner works while another looks on with a safety lamp, the workings of which are shown below.

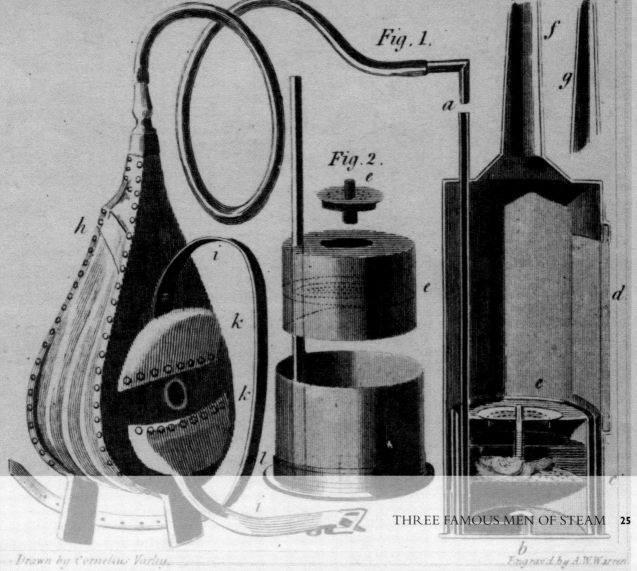

Fig. 1.

Fig. 2.

Drawn by Cornelius Varley.

Engrav'd by A.W. Warren

George Stephenson
instructing navvies on site.

Thames at Wandsworth Creek and Croydon. Known as the Surrey Iron Railway it began life in 1801 with a track length of twenty-six miles. Worked by horses or donkeys the line failed to make a profit, despite an income from charges levied on the public for moving their own goods.

Nearly twenty years later a second but more famous public railway, the Stockton and Darlington, was created largely through the efforts of a group of Quaker businessmen led by Edward Pease of Darlington. The initial plan had been for a horse-drawn tramway, but in 1821 Mr Pease had been visited at his home by Nicholas Wood, viewer at Killingworth and George Stephenson, the engine wright.

With the help of his more eloquent companion, George made a successful application to become the engineer of the proposed line. He also extolled the virtues of his steam engines. Mr Pease visited Killingworth, had a ride on an engine and, not only did he get George appointed to the post but also obtained an alteration to the Stockton and Darlington act of 1821, so that in 1823 it allowed the use of steam engines to haul goods and passengers over the line. Edward Pease also agreed to invest in Stephenson's plan to build a 'locomotive manufactory' in Newcastle. George put up the one thousand pounds that had been presented to him for his miners' safety lamp.

Assisted by his son, Robert, as chainman, George made his preliminary survey, and the gauge was settled at four foot eight and a half inches. Wrought or malleable iron rail imported from Sweden was his preferred choice, but some use had to be made of cast iron rails initially for reason of economy. Work commenced on the line in 1822, and the locomotive works was set up to build engines by 1824, with Robert at the drawing board. Three of Stephenson's engines were ordered for the new railway. However Robert, who had obtained a position as a mining engineer in Colombia, left England and the newly opened locomotive works in June of that year, and set sail for South America. George had made him undergo a medical examination of some intensity before he left, probably hoping to prevent his son's departure, but, medical notwithstanding, off he went on a three year contract at the age of twenty-one. He left his father to cope with a self imposed workload that became heavier every year that his son was absent. Determined to be recognised as the man most suitable for each and every post that called for an engineer with experience in the new technology

of railways, on 25th May 1824 George had secured the appointment as engineer to the proposed Liverpool and Manchester Railway just a month before Robert departed. So it was that George was deprived of his son's emotional and practical help at a time when the completion of the Stockton and Darlington was in sight, and his humiliation before the committee considering the Liverpool and Manchester bill in March 1825 was yet to come.

Through the efforts of his father Robert had been provided with a useful theoretical and practical training in engineering. In 1821 he had assisted the superintending of the construction of the Hetton Railway. He had taken part in the initial survey of the Stockton and Darlington, and had assisted Mr William James with his survey of the proposed Liverpool and Manchester Railway. The following year he had assisted George with the working survey of the Stockton and Darlington, and in 1823 he helped to set up the locomotive works at Newcastle. In the early part of 1824 Robert had completed designs for a stationary engine for the S & D rope hauled incline at Brusselton. This wealth of experience had made Robert a prime target for the 'head hunters' of the day, desperate for engineers for the mines of South America.

George Stephenson replaced Mr James as surveyor of the Liverpool and Manchester when that gentleman suffered imprisonment for debt. By this time, George had superintended the construction of nine railways and had built fifty-five engines, of which sixteen were steam locomotives. Mr James had faced relentless opposition and obstruction to his work from the landowners and those with coaching and canal interests. Stephenson and his assistants fared no better, and his plans and estimates proved to be imperfect. Some had been done in haste, others had been done by moonlight. His assessment of the costs did not accord with works as shown in the plans, but were sometimes based on a later solution that had not yet been included. Against the advice of the L & M directors George failed to hide his enthusiasm for the use of steam locomotives on the line. He often mentioned potentially alarming speeds of above four or five miles an hour in his replies to questions. Also, there was not an established engineer he could call on who would support his intention to build the railway across Chat Moss and run steam locomotives over it. Chat Moss was such a waterlogged and unstable bog that in 1821 Mr James, having sunk into it with his theodolite, could only save himself by laying down and rolling himself to firmer ground and the helping hands of Robert Stephenson.

Although the preamble was passed by one vote, the Bill to make the railway was rejected by the Commons committee and was withdrawn by its promoters. The enquiry had lasted more than two months. Stephenson was seriously depressed, not only by the lost opportunities but also because during the enquiry another engineer, William Cubitt, had been called by the L & M directors to correct George's estimates. One of his young surveyors, Hugh Steele, later committed suicide in Stephenson's office.

Despite his low spirits Stephenson had continued to build steam locomotives, and four months later Locomotion No. 1 was completed at the Stephenson company works in Newcastle, in time to haul a party of directors on a trial run from Shildon to Darlington on 26th September 1825. George was present while his brother, James, drove the engine. Locomotion weighed about six and a half tons. It had a wrought iron boiler with a single flue from the firebrick lined furnace. This single tube did not transmit enough heat into the water to avoid the occasional red hot chimney. It was fitted with two cylinders with each one

Crowds gather to watch the opening of the Stockton and Darlington Railway.

let into the boiler top in line with an axle. The pistons transmitted their power to the relevant wheel via parallel beams and long connecting rod to the crank pins. Coupling rods kept the back and front wheels in phase, and to ensure reliable starting (no dead centres) the crank pins on the rear wheels were ninety degrees behind those on the leading wheels. For this reason, the coupling rod pins on the rear wheels were on return cranks. No springs were fitted though three point suspension was provided which would have improved traction. A four wheeled tender carried 240 gallons of water and 15 cwt of coal.

On Tuesday, 27th September 1825 the Stockton and Darlington Railway officially opened. At 06.00 a.m. the directors watched Robert Stephenson's stationary engine at Brusselton as it lifted a train of wagons up an incline more than a mile in length in just seven and a half minutes. Eight minutes later the wagons were at the foot of the opposite incline where Locomotion No.1, driven by George Stephenson, waited for the wagons to be added to his train. Coupled to his engine were six wagons loaded with coals or flour, then there was a coach for the directors and proprietors, next there were twenty-one empty coal

wagons crowded with passengers and lastly the six wagons of coal from the incline.

When George started the train it was preceded by a horseman carrying a flag. On reaching a favourable gradient George told the rider to get out of the way, and Locomotion and her train carried on to Darlington reaching speeds of up to fifteen miles an hour on the way. The train carried 453 people and weighed 93 tons. On the return journey 600 people rode in the train, some of the loaded coal wagons having been replaced by empties. On less favourable gradients the twelve mile journey took three hours. However, the time probably flew by as they carried a band of musicians, and the route was lined with onlookers and riders on horseback. Everyone had been given a holiday for the occasion. A dinner at the Town Hall in Stockton ended a long and triumphant day for George and his friends.

Initially 'travelling engines' were not the primary source of motive power on the S & D. The public had access to the railway and horse-drawn traffic predominated, and the steepest gradients were operated by fixed stationary engines. Stephenson's first passenger coach constructed in October

A horseman carries a flag in front of the train on the Stockton and Darlington Railway.

1825 and named Experiment, was also horse-drawn, and horse-drawn coaches could cover twelve miles in sixty minutes. The general 'cut and thrust' up and down such a shared system eventually forced the proprietors of the Railway to take over the running of the line themselves.

In the meantime, undaunted by the failure of their first Bill, the L & M directors planned a second application for the 1826 Parliamentary session. George was replaced by Messrs George and John Rennie, engineers, and Charles Vignoles to survey and plan the line. The use of steam locomotives did not feature in this Bill, and

to minimise the destruction of roads and houses it was proposed that Liverpool would be entered via a tunnel, which also avoided some obstructive private estates. The Bill was passed on this occasion and George was soon reappointed as engineer to carry out the work, his first priority being to cross Chat Moss. Work began in 1826 and initial attempts appeared to be a great waste of time and materials, as everything sunk without trace into the depths of the bog. In Newcastle, George's preoccupation with Chat Moss meant that Timothy Hackworth at Shildon had to turn the new locomotives and their drivers into

reliable performers. L T C Rolt writes "...Hackworth was the world's first shedmaster..." and Shildon men were to take their expertise around the world. It was also the partial cause of his locomotive company running into financial difficulties, to the consternation of Edward Pease. Subsequently Pease contacted Robert in Colombia urging to return home, which he did in 1827. After four years, during which time it had often seemed that the twelve square mile bog could never bear a railway track let alone the weight of a train, Stephenson's methods ultimately proved to be successful. Against all contemporary engineering opinion he had laid down a floating bed of hurdles made from branches and stuffed with dried heather. These were then topped with fine stone, over which the track was laid. Chat Moss was conquered and the railway was completed on 1st January 1830.

Much of the rest of the line had been completed before 1830, major works included a mile and a half long tunnel into Liverpool and the 100 foot deep cutting made through rock at Mount Olive. Stephenson's preference for steam hauled trains was not shared by other professional engineers, and the L & M directors were divided by conflicting advice. However, in 1828 Stephenson was allowed to build a locomotive that was used during the final stage of the line's completion. A decision was made that engine builders should be given

the chance to demonstrate the efficiency and suitability of their machines at a public trial to be held in October 1829 over a section of the line already laid at Rainhill. A prize of £500.00 was offered.

Stephenson's Newcastle works produced Rocket, a 'racy' looking four wheeled engine designed by Robert Stephenson and Henry Booth. It was a major departure from the heavy 'Killingworth colliery' style. It had large (4' 8") single driving wheels and small trailing wheels. The boiler was only six feet long but it had twenty-five three inch diameter flue tubes between its water jacketed external fire box and the tall chimney. Two inclined cylinders drove crankpins on the driving wheels, and exhaust steam aided the combustion process by being released up the chimney. A four wheeled tender carrying fuel and water was attached. The multiple tube innovation had been suggested by Henry Booth.

The trials attracted thousands of onlookers. Each engine had to complete ten trips travelling at a minimum speed of ten miles per hour over a short section of the line. After some attention to the engine a further ten trips were to be completed. There were two other competing machines, one being Timothy Hackworth's Sans Pareil, an old fashioned four coupled engine with a return flue boiler. It had two vertical cylinders the exhaust from which was piped up the chimney, and was sharpened by constriction of the pipe end. The other engine was Novelty, a light machine more akin to a road carriage than a locomotive. It had a horizontal and vertical boiler and a vertical piston driving the wheels through a

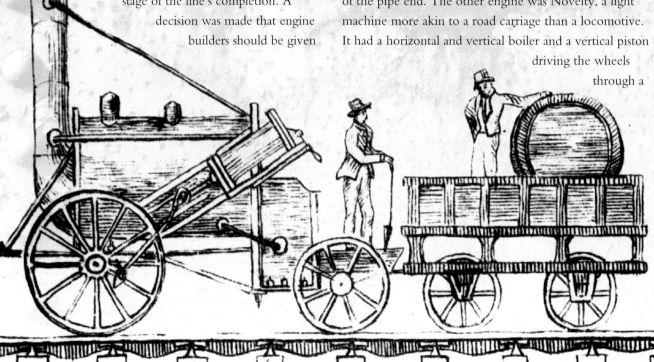

Left and Below:
Stephenson's Rocket,
winner of the prize for best
locomotive at the Rainhill
trials, on the Liverpool and
Manchester Railway.

bell crank. Bellows were provided to stimulate the fire. Novelty was built by Messrs Braithwaite and Ericsson. Rocket successfully performed all the required tests and reached a top speed of twenty-nine miles an hour. Robert Stephenson and Henry Booth shared the £500.00 prize money. Novelty, which had reached thirty miles an hour, set light to her bellows and was forced to retire. Although too heavy for the four wheeled class Sans Pareil was allowed to run, but broke down during the trials as she was unable to maintain water feed to the boiler. Also, Sans Pareil's fuel consumption was unduly high because the design of the sharpened exhaust blast caused a considerable portion of her fire to be ejected up the chimney.

It was as a result of the Rainhill trials that the steam locomotive came to eventually replace the horse. During the twelve month period between September 1829 and September 1830, Robert Stephenson continued to improve the basic design of each subsequent engine turned out of the works. With the eighth engine Northumbrian which had a separate smokebox the Rocket type had fully evolved from its Killingworth ancestors.

The Liverpool and Manchester Railway was officially opened on 15th September 1830

Civil engineer Joseph Locke.

when the most modern engine, Northumbrian, driven by George Stephenson, pulled out of Liverpool with the first of eight trains conveying a total of six hundred people. Robert drove No. 6 Phoenix, George's older brother, also Robert, drove No. 7 North Star. No. 1 Rocket was driven by Joseph Locke, No. 5 Dart was driven by Thomas Gooch, William Alleard drove No. 3 Comet, Frederick Swanwick drove No. 4 Arrow and Anthony Harding drove No. 2 Meteor.

The special trains used both tracks and during the stop for water at Parkway, the Duke of Wellington's train, drawn

A train passes under Rainhill Bridge on the Liverpool and Manchester Railway.

by Northumbrian, waited to be passed by other trains. The pro-railway and pro-steam MP William Huskisson was unfortunately run over by Rocket as he attempted to scramble up into the Duke's train. George Stephenson had the injured and dying man lifted aboard Northumbrian, which was unhooked to speed off for medical help at Eccles. George worked his engine up to thirty-six miles an hour during that desperate journey, though in later life he was to express his opinion that train speeds should be kept to forty miles an hour. He warned that metals could fracture under the strains involved, and one wonders if his appreciation of this danger had lurked unpleasantly at the back of his mind during the dash for help in 1830. Mr Huskisson died that night of his injuries.

During the next three months Stephenson's engines hauled fifty thousand passengers sharing 954 runs between Liverpool and Manchester. At the age of 49 George was vindicated in his steadfast advocation of the travelling steam engine. His services as supervising engineer were sought on all sides as business men of the day formed companies to connect their towns by rail. He also retained an interest and talent for mining. George had recommended that Robert, then 27, be retained as engineer of a sixteen mile railway between Leicester and a coal producing area near Swannington. While surveying the line Robert realised that coal deposits were to be found near Ashby-de-la-Zouch, below Snibston. The new railway would earn money by moving coal, the land above it was for sale. George and

William Huskisson who was tragically killed at the opening of the Liverpool and Manchester Railway.

some of his Liverpool friends purchased the estate in 1831 and after some determined digging and the exercise of George's mechanical expertise, the coal layer was finally reached in 1832. In order to be near the work George had moved from Liverpool to make a home at Alton Grange. He created a village at the mine with houses, schools, church and chapel for the miners and their families.

The promoters of the London and Birmingham Railway had sought Stephenson's advice in 1830 with regard to the route the line should take. There were the usual difficulties with landowners and horse breeders in 1832. The Railway's promoters had to triple the money

The Liverpool and Manchester Railway enters Manchester across Water Street.

they offered to buy the land they needed, so that in 1833 a reintroduced Bill was passed by both Commons and Lords committees. On George's advice Robert, who had married Frances Sanderson in 1829, was made chief engineer of the L & B at a salary of £1500.00 per annum. Although the construction of this one hundred and twelve mile railway demanded great civil engineering skills, the line was completed in 1838.

The years between 1834 and 1837 were the busiest of George's life. During this period he covered twenty thousand miles by post chaise from Alton Grange. He visited Ireland and Scotland, and made journeys to his London office that was opened in 1836. He was engaged as engineer on the North Midland Railway, from Derby to Leeds and opened in 1840; the Normanton and York, opened 1840; the Manchester and Leeds, opened 1840; the Birmingham and Derby, opened 1839 and the Sheffield to Rotherham, opened 1839. He also advised on railway construction in Europe. In 1835 King Leopold of Belgium made George a Knight of the Order of Leopold at a public ceremony honouring the 'father of railways'. Never at ease with letter writing, George sometimes dictated to his

Pumps draining the Kilsby Tunnel of quick sand during construction of the London and Birmingham Railway.

secretary as many as thirty-seven letters a day, and on one occasion for twelve hours continuously. In 1838 he was engaged on the Chester to Holyhead survey, and in 1841 he moved his home for the final time to Tapton House, near Chesterfield Green. Once again he was using his mining talents. He made a pit at Clay Cross to extract coal and at Ambergate he developed a quarry to make lime.

Locomotives constructed at the Stephensons' company works were sold to a worldwide market. Adaptations of the innovative Patentee design of 1834 were the basis of the most successful locomotives on broad or standard gauge throughout the world. The fifteen year 'Battle of the Gauges', during which speeds of over seventy miles an hour were recorded, was eventually settled in favour of Stephenson's four foot eight and a half inch Standard Gauge, which he had stipulated for the Stockton and Darlington. In 1842 George was working on an idea he had for a self braking system suitable for higher speeds.

The 'Railway Mania' of 1845 resulted in an extraordinary change in attitude with regard to railway building. The battles George had fought to gain acceptance for his concepts of railway and steam locomotion were a

thing of the past, everybody wanted to invest in even the most crazy schemes. Between 1844 and 1846 440 railway acts were passed by the House of Commons, and more than £180 million pounds of new railway capital was authorised. A complete reversal of the land owners' attitude to railways had taken place, George was besieged in his son's London office by speculators that wanted his name on a prospectus.

George was also an honoured visitor to Belgium, and in August 1845 he reported on the proposed route of the West Flanders Railway. As early as 1835 he and Robert had been asked by King Leopold for advice on the construction

of a railway system that would open up the ports to the vast reserves of coal and minerals within the country. In 1837, when the line between Brussels and Ghent was opened, George and his party were the honoured guests at the ceremonies, processions, dinners and public ball which celebrated the occasion.

In September 1845 George travelled to Spain to examine the route of the proposed Royal North of Spain Railway. He was taking time out from the supervision of his Clay Cross collieries, having agreed to a six week absence while being paid for his expenses only. After many

A platform at Euston Station, terminus of the London and Birmingham Railway.

Stephenson's first successful steam engine, the property of Hetton Colliery, takes part in a centenary procession, 1925.

long days of surveying from dawn to dusk, sometimes sleeping the night on dirt floors, George advised Sir Joshua Walmsley that the terrain was difficult and that the expected level of traffic could not justify investment unless land, labour (convicts) and timber were provided to the company. They waited ten days for a decision from the Spanish government, but as no such decision was forthcoming, Walmsley withdrew his offer. The railway company was later dissolved.

George returned to England, travelling almost continually day and night, determined to arrive by the 30th November. The strain that he had put himself under had weakened him and he was seen to be ill when the group reached Paris. During the voyage from Havre to Southampton he developed pleurisy and they had to bleed him. Once at home, George recovered gradually, but he was a weakened man after that trip.

In 1847 George was a guest of Prime Minister Sir Robert Peel at his mansion at Drayton Manor. He made a speech contrasting the change in attitudes of land owners towards railways between 1825 and 1847. He also took a crack at Brunel's determination to do everything differently. George derided the Great Western's broad gauge engines with the boiler on one carriage and the engine on another,

the ten foot wheels which were supposed to go at 100 miles per hour, the steep gradients and the atmospheric system. "Our North Star engine was called upon to carry the traffic. It did double duty, though engines, like horses, need a rest." Perhaps Sir Robert flushed as he heard this as he had supported many of those ideas.

In 1848, while keeping an eye on his colliery interests, George enjoyed his life at Tapton House. He involved himself in horticulture and farming, and indulged in his boyhood interests in the study of birds and animals. On 26th July 1848 he visited the Mechanics Institute at Birmingham to read his paper on the 'Fallacies of the Rotatary Engine'. However it seemed that his lungs had never regained their health and, back at Tapton, bouts of fever culminated in a massive haemorrhage of his lungs which finally killed him on 12th August 1848, at the age of sixty-seven.

He was buried at Trinity Church, Chesterfield. A statue that had been commissioned by the boards of the Liverpool and Manchester and Grand Junction Railway companies two years previously, arrived from Rome shortly after his death and was placed in St George's Hall, Liverpool. A second statue was put in the original and very imposing Great Hall of Euston Station.

Robert Stephenson

GRAND OVERSEER

A large and sensitive portrait of the Stephensons hangs in the Institute of Civil Engineers, Great George Street, London. To a life-long locomotive man like myself it arouses something of the awe and affection that churchgoers feel when they contemplate a religious icon. After all it depicts the prophet of the steam locomotive, the father of a clan of enginemen that would spread worldwide from harsh Northumbrian roots. By his side the son that improved and developed the older man's concepts. I have a copy of the painting in my library.

The Stephensons are often referred to as 'Messrs Stephenson'. It is difficult to write of one man without getting entangled in the activities of the other. Their lives and achievements form a complex pattern, a pattern that is the result of George's systematic way of tackling his problems. We see it demonstrated in accounts of George's early work to improve the efficiencies of pumping engines, and later in his retirement years when he applied his mind to the production of the perfect cucumber! Just like a prize winning vegetable from his father's greenhouse, George's son was 'shaped' by early and appropriate training in order to develop the skills

Robert and his father George, who forged his education.

Civil engineer Robert Stephenson.

and knowledge most beneficial to his father's business.

Robert learned mining skills as an apprentice to Nicholas Wood at West Moors. Surveying skills were developed while helping his father on the Hetton Colliery project. In 1822 he had assisted William James for twelve months with his survey of the Liverpool and Manchester Railway. He also assisted George with the Stockton and Darlington survey, even deputising for the older man during Parliamentary appearances when he was only eighteen years of age.

The education that George gave to his son forged a 'key' to the doors that had been closed to him by his own lack of formal schooling. To the quick, intuitive observance of the father was added the son's growing ability to refine, explain and develop ideas that formed in George's canny mind. Only once did Robert depart from

Newcastle area in the 1820s.

this role, when he took a brief 'holiday' from 1824 to 1827 in South America.

On 23rd June 1823 at just twenty years of age, Robert had been made the managing partner of the locomotive and engine building works, "Robert Stephenson and Company". As we have seen, this was a partnership between the Quakers, Edward Pease and Michael Longdon, and George and Robert Stephenson. Robert had just

returned to Newcastle after a short spell at Edinburgh University. Pease loaned him £500 for the purchase of shares, and Robert was made responsible for setting up production and engaging workmen. For this he was paid a salary of £200 per annum. In 1823 both George and Robert travelled extensively, visiting London, Bristol, parts of Shropshire and even Ireland in the hunt for orders to be fulfilled at the Newcastle works.

In April 1824 Robert once again visited London to see the Stockton and Darlington Act through Parliament. It appears that at this time he became acquainted with Fanny Sanderson, the daughter of a city merchant. In May, just as he was completing drawings of the stationary engine for the Brusselton incline, he was offered a contract to re-open gold and silver mines in South America for the Colombian Mining Association of London. For some time experienced engineers had been 'head hunted' for such schemes. Some ten years earlier Richard Trevithick had sailed to Peru to mine for gold, though no-one had heard from him since!

To Robert it must have appeared that there was a fortune to be made by using his skills as a miner, a surveyor and a steam engineer. Perhaps he thought that Mr Sanderson would look with favour upon a young man who had made himself some money by his own enterprise. Perhaps he just wanted adventure and some freedom from a controlling parent and those bossy Quakers? Whatever his reasons, Robert was sufficiently tempted by the offer to declare to his partners that he would only be away for twelve months when he had in fact signed a three year contract.

Robert carefully prepared for his new project by having some surveying instruments made to his order. George, who was busy in Liverpool working on the foundations of the Liverpool and Manchester Railway, arranged that Michael Longdon would take over Robert's duties for the twelve months his son would be abroad. Robert travelled from London to Liverpool in a dangerously overloaded stagecoach, where he said goodbye to his father on the quay side.

Robert set sail on 8th June 1824. The name of the ship, Sir William Congreve was rather more appropriate than at first apparent. Well known for his invention of the clock with the zigzag rolling ball escapement which also bears his name, Sir William Congreve was at the time far more famous for his rocket propelled ordnance. Fired from especially adapted ships or from land from a sort of tripod, these rockets had a range of some two miles and proved to be very effective against the French in the later stages of the Napoleonic wars. They were also used against the Americans in 1812. While being very effective against an enemy, Congreve rockets were also prone to premature explosion and were no doubt highly dangerous. One writer, alarmed at the potential speed of George's steam locomotives, warned that "to travel at twice the speed of a stagecoach would be as ridiculous ... as being fired off in

Miners at work at the entrance of a mine.

one of Congreve's ricochet-rockets", no doubt reasoning that both inventions 'phizzed' loudly. It surely follows that the sardonic Geordie humour of the Stephensons caused them to name their most famous engine Rocket.

The so-called roads of Colombia were more like bridleways along and up which mules carried everything. Everything including Robert and his small party which set out on a 1200 mile trek from Caracas to Santa Fe de Bogota, the capital of Colombia in the foothills of the Eastern Cordillera, to meet the commercial manager of the Mining Association. He continued on to the area of operation at the ancient Spanish City of Maniquita, where the completely overgrown and abandoned mines were located. At every step he was hindered by false information from guides who promised rich deposits of ore which seldom materialised. The local authorities had to be treated to extravagant social gatherings, and trouble frequently broke out between the rowdy Cornish miners and their North country engineer in charge.

Although Robert had, with his uncle Robert in February and March of 1824, taken the trouble to visit Cornish mines to familiarise himself with their working methods before leaving England, this did not impress the Cornish miners. Often drunk, they derided his abilities and refused to take his orders. His warning letters to the Mining Association in London were ignored, and heavy equipment continued to arrive, only to be piled up alongside the narrow mule paths that flanked the River Magdalena. He suffered fever and depression and, although he had eventually set up a house on the eastern slopes of the Andes where the temperatures were a reasonable 75°, he keenly felt the lack of a decent library and well equipped laboratory. Letters from England told him of lost orders at Robert Stephenson and Co. due to bad workmanship, and that his father was under attack for the botched survey of the Liverpool and Manchester Railway. Edward Pease wanted out of the partnership but George could not afford to buy his share. All in all it was a sorry state of affairs and, to cap it all by 1826 the South American mining speculations also began to fail.

The Mining Association tried to get George to give his permission for Robert to stay a while longer, at least until a successor could be found. But father and son had both had enough, and in June 1827 Robert made the return voyage via New York, arriving in Liverpool in November that year to meet the white haired George, now 46 years old. On his way, Robert had chanced to meet the destitute Richard Trevithick and was able to loan him the £50 he needed for a passage back to England.

The South American 'adventure' taught Robert several lessons which ultimately hardened him until he was able to present a steely eye to those who failed to meet with his expectations. However, away from his professional career, the young engineer was often lonely and depressed, surrounded by the malign forces of nature and duplicitous mankind. It is possible that he sought the comfort of narcotics at this time. In later life he was advised by friends to cut down on his habit. He was often 'hipped'. Those great and tireless men who died young may have depended heavily on substances that were more acceptable in the early nineteenth century than they became in the twentieth.

Be that as it may, his competent presence back in Newcastle brought a swift improvement to the fortune and reputation of the Robert Stephenson and Co. locomotive works. The primitive Killingworth engines were supplanted and the prize winning design of No. 1 Rocket had, by loco No. 8 Northumbrian, begun to develop into the modern locomotive with its separate smokebox and cylinders almost parallel with the ground.

Further improvements followed. The Planet had a cranked driving axle and inside cylinders beneath the smokebox. The Patentee had a set of wheels behind the driving wheels to support a large firebox, and it was this design of 1834 which really set a worldwide standard for locomotive design at the time. In 1837 R S & Co.'s 150th engine North Star became No. 1 to the fledgling Great Western Railway. It was a most efficient engine and one which Daniel Gooch was to use as the basis for some very

A lithograph of Stephenson's Rocket.

The Rocket in her later, modified form.

successful broad gauge locomotives.

In 1842 Robert Stephenson adopted and patented the link motion invented by one of his pattern makers, William Howe. For the first time the expansive use of steam was possible and engine No. 71 could be reversed in the dark by any driver. To avoid paying patent dues, Daniel Gooch of the Great Western Railway made his own version of Stephenson's link motion by substituting a fixed link and fitting a radius rod that could be raised or lowered.

In the same year Robert decided to lengthen the boilers of his engines from 9 feet to 13 feet in order to reduce the working temperature of their smokeboxes, and to avoid the problem of their chimneys becoming red hot. By 1846 150 engines of his 'long boiler' patent were in use, though they were found to be mainly suited to freight work due to their instability at speed. The inventive William Howe produced a scheme for a three cylindered engine with three sets of valve gear, which Stephenson patented as a Stephenson-Howe design.

Concurrently with the improvements he was making to

his locomotives, Robert was also involved with various civil engineering activities. Among other projects, he attended to the Canterbury and Whitstable Railway and, in 1829, the sixteen mile Leicester and Swannington Railway. He joined the Institute of Civil Engineers, and he and George were appointed joint engineers of the London and Birmingham Railway. By this time George had recovered from the humiliation he had suffered for the poor survey of the Liverpool

and Manchester Railway. In January 1830 he had the deep satisfaction of driving Rocket over the 'uncrossable' Chat Moss. However, George's finest talents did not lie in the day to day organisation of major works and on 14th June 1830, the 26 year old Robert was left in sole charge of the London to Birmingham survey. From 1833 Robert battled to complete the L & B, which was eventually achieved after a further five years, during which time Robert estimated that he had walked the 112 mile length of the line no fewer than fifteen times.

It was an incredible display of his ability to overcome

The stationary engine chimneys and locomotive engine house near Camden Town on the London and Birmingham Railway.

the many problems inherent in such an undertaking. The route was divided into thirty sections, for which individual contractors agreed on a price and completion date. Sometimes the geological make up of the ridges through which they had to cut or tunnel delayed progress. Costs could mount beyond initial estimates and it was not uncommon for contractors to find themselves bankrupted.

Robert was obliged to complete seven of the sections using railway company labour in order to keep to his timetable. Especially trying were the works at Tring which required long cuttings some 60 feet deep; Kilsby, where

thirteen pumping engines (at George's suggestion) removed 2,000 gallons of water every minute for eight months to dry the quicksands that were inundating the tunnel bores. Other particularly difficult sections of the line included Wolverton, Blisworth, Rugby and Coventry.

Although Robert missed the target date of January 1838, the line was officially opened in September that year. He rode the open footplate of the Directors' special during the inaugural run from London to Birmingham, where he and fellow dignitaries later dined at Dee's Royal Hotel.

The Directors appointed Robert Engineer-in-Chief of

The headgear shaft of Kilsby Tunnel.

Broken sleepers and pieces of stone on the track in the great ventilation shaft at Kilsby Tunnel.

the London to Birmingham line, at a salary of £1,500 per annum. He had proved himself to be a great civil engineer, achieving independence from his father while adding lustre to the name of their railway construction company, George Stephenson and Son. Clients from abroad now honoured them and sought their advice.

By 1840 Robert was a wealthy man living a comfortable life at his home at Haverstock Hill with Fanny, his wife of eleven years. His achievements were suddenly and brutally turned to ashes when Fanny was diagnosed with cancer. Two years later she died. They had no children.

As though this personal tragedy was not enough, Robert was also being hounded by creditors of the failed Stanhope and Tyne Railway. He had accepted shares in the railway in lieu of his fee for acting as consulting engineer in 1832. However, the company was not incorporated and as it could no longer pay its debts the creditors turned to the shareholders for redress. Robert's wealth made him a prime target and his liabilities were potentially unlimited. It was a very nasty situation, though he eventually managed to sort it out by organising the formation of an incorporated company which took over the Stanhope and Tyne under

the name of Pontop and South Shields Railway Company. Robert did not risk buying shares in any subsequent railway scheme, and those shares he had he sold before the great crash of railway stocks.

Any remaining liabilities were covered when George Hudson's Newcastle and Darlington Junction Railway made use of the path of the Pontop and South Shields in order to at last unite London with Newcastle in 1844. George Stephenson, who had always promoted such a link with London, and Robert were in Hudson's 'Grand Opening Train' on 18th June 1844. There was the

inevitable banquet, and workers from Robert Stephenson and Co. paraded through the town waving banners.

Robert's next great works were to be the bridges and viaducts required in order to lay routes to the north of Newcastle that had been selected by George to construct a line to Berwick and Edinburgh.

Unlike George, Robert was diffident about taking all the credit for these great works. He had probably learned the hard way that Hubris precedes Nemesis in the affairs of engineers as surely as they did in the affairs of Greek heroes. As a result, when he made a bad mistake, as he did with

The famous Doric Arch that marked the entrance to the London and Birmingham Railway's Euston Terminus.

Scottish engineer James
Naismith and his patented
steam hammer.

The opening of the high level railway bridge at Newcastle-Upon-Tyne.

the Dee Bridge at Chester which collapsed under a train in 1847, damage to his reputation was less than it might have been had fellow professionals harboured spiteful feelings towards him.

Throughout his career he had confided his attacks of self doubt to others, especially when facing unexpected geological or engineering difficulties. He often sought the help of brother engineers and gave his support in return when asked for it. His responsibilities had mushroomed with George's semi-retirement after 1840, and must have given him many a sleepless night. At one point he was attending to thirty-three different new schemes.

On 6th October 1846, the first piles for his high level rail and road bridge between Gateshead and Newcastle station, were driven in at the rate of thirty-two feet in four minutes by Naismith's newly invented steam hammer. This hammer had also been invaluable in the construction of Brunel's huge iron ships. Opened in August 1849 the bridge spanned 515 feet of river and a ravine that had many buildings clinging to its steep slopes.

A graceful twenty-eight arch viaduct over the Tweed at Berwick was completed in 1847. For the Chester to Holyhead line (surveyed by George in 1838) Robert designed his famous Conway and Britannia bridges, the

Stephenson's viaduct over the river Tweed.

foundation stones for which were laid in 1846.

In order to create spans of great strength and at navigable heights, Robert enlisted the expertise of William Fairburn, a shipbuilder at Millwall and a one time work mate of his father in his coal pit days. The rectangular tubes of wrought iron were riveted together on the banks of the river. At Conway, two 400 foot tubes, each 1,180 tons in weight. For the Britannia bridge two tubes 1,524 feet long, each weighing 1,600 tons with 450 tons of rivets in each tube.

The tubes were floated into position under a scheme devised by Mr Evans who was contracted to build the bridge at Conway. In order to position the tube laden pontoons Robert relied on the skills of Captain Claxton, who directed sailors used to managing ropes, cables and capstans in a manner that no landlubber could equal. Claxton had also been of great assistance to Brunel when his steam ship Great Eastern had stuck fast at Dundrum Bay. Now Brunel and his Captain were with Robert as he

Robert Stephenson's Britannia Bridge under construction.

The entrance to the
Britannia Tubular Bridge.

ERECTED ANNO DOMINI MDCC
ROBERT STEPHENSON ENGINEER

prepared to battle with tides and winds to position those great tubes. Present among the many spectators was a very frail George Stephenson, who had but four months more to live. By April 1848 the first 400 foot tube was in place to be raised cautiously by hydraulic rams. The second tube was installed by January of the following year.

The Britannia Bridge at Anglesey was similarly erected, and was officially opened on 18th March 1850 when three

locomotives hauled a 500 ton train through the completed tube. The second tube and its track were completed in October 1851. Robert also designed tubular bridges for the Alexandria and Cairo Railway in Egypt and in 1853 acted as engineer in chief for the construction of the Victoria Bridge in Canada. This 6,588 tubular bridge crossed the St Lawrence River at Montreal. Work started in April 1854 but the bridge was not to be completed until 24th

The Menai Suspension Bridge, designed by Thomas Telford, and the Britannia Tubular Bridge, designed by Robert Stephenson, between mainland Wales and Anglesey.

November 1859, shortly after Robert's death.

During the final years of his life Robert discovered the missing element that released him from lonely responsibility. He did not marry again and he remained childless. The steam yacht Titania became the love of his life, on board which he spent many weeks at sea in the company of friends. He had the first Titania built in 1850 but it was destroyed by fire at Cowes in 1852. His second

Titania was bigger at 184 tons and had a large saloon library. He loved reading and collecting fine art. A final voyage to northern England took him to visit his childhood haunts on the Tyne, and to the scene of his most recent effort at Holyhead. With winter approaching he sailed to Egypt in October 1858, eventually meeting up with Brunel, who was accompanied by his wife and son Henry. They shared Christmas dinner at the Hotel D'Orient. At

The construction of
the Victoria Railway
Bridge across the
St Lawrence river,
Montreal, Canada,.

the time, both men were suffering from a chronic nephritis known as 'Bright's disease'.

By February 1859 Robert was back in London. In the summer of that year he suffered poor health, yet still managed to sail to Norway in the autumn to attend a banquet held in celebration of the completion of another new railway. It was during this banquet that Robert's health took a sudden turn for the worse and he returned to England with some haste. The following month, October 1859, Robert Stephenson died at his home in Gloucester Square. His death was widely mourned, and the funeral cortege travelled through Hyde Park to Westminster Abbey where his body was placed in the nave next to the grave of another great engineer, Thomas Telford. On the great rivers of Thames, Tyne, Wear and Tees all shipping lay silent with their flags at half mast. The 1,500 employees of Robert Stephenson and Co. marched to a memorial service in the church of St Nicholas in Newcastle. One of his pallbearers was Joseph Locke, who had succeeded him as President of the Institute of Civil Engineers.

Robert Stephenson shortly before his death.

Brunel
THE HEROIC
ENGINEER

Brunel was undoubtedly a visionary, he wrote of his tendency to build castles in the air. He was also a great Chief of Staff and could inspire the perfect team to drive forward the most complex projects. He was certainly a hero who showed great bravery facing physical dangers and in facing the responsibilities that resulted from attributes one and two above. His engineering and architectural constructions were heroic in their scale and grandeur. His final battle and early death at the age of fifty-three calls to mind the story of Captain Mahab's fatal pursuit of the leviathan in Herman Melville's *Moby Dick*. His final

creation, the SS Great Eastern, had originally been called 'Leviathan' and the last photograph of Brunel standing bareheaded before its funnel is as tragic as the image of Captain Mahab inextricably caught up and doomed by his obsession with the great white whale.

One cannot help warming to Brunel as a human being. Visionaries like George Stephenson can be prickly characters who are jealous of their status as formulators of unarguable truths. A man like Robert Stephenson who was shaped by his father to fulfil a role, who having lost his wife, committed himself to a childless and work-centred

Brunel's steamship the SS Great Eastern was launched in 1858.

Civil engineer Isambard
Kingdom Brunel.

Marc Isambard Brunel.

life, somehow lacks the appeal of a Victorian family man such as Brunel. Eighteen Duke Street was both Brunel's office and his source of relaxation. It was his home from the day of his marriage to the day he died, with his family around him.

Two hundred years ago on 9th May 1806, Isambard Kingdom Brunel was born at Portsmouth. His father, Marc Isambard Brunel, was an engineer from France. His mother, Sophia Kingdom, although English was living in France when she met Marc. Brunel senior had a talent for invention which had been successfully used to increase the production of ships' rigging blocks for the British Royal Navy. As a young man he had met Sophia in Rouen while serving as an officer in the French Navy. Unsympathetic to the revolution he had moved to America in 1793 where he worked as a surveyor and engineer. Later he was granted American citizenship and he became the chief engineer for New York. He moved to England in 1799 in order to put his inventive genius at the service of the Navy administration. Sophia, who had been imprisoned by the French from the start of their hostilities with England, eventually managed to return to London in 1795. She began corresponding with Marc while he was in America and they married when he returned to England in 1799.

The outline above is brief, but illustrates the very cosmopolitan and romantic background from which our third engineer, Isambard, emerged. He father was a creative engineer with an affinity for naval matters. Isambard's unrelenting tendency to reject the conventional approach may also stem from this background, as does his final enthusiastic involvement in the building of large steam powered ships.

Like Robert, his early education was organised by his father so as to make best use of his inborn talents. From an early age he was good at mathematics and was interested in surveying. At home the family were hosts to notable men of science. Marc was elected to the Royal Society in 1814. Babbage, Faraday and Sir Humphry Davy were his

friends. From the age of eight Isambard studied at Dr Morrell's boarding school in Hove. In 1820 he continued his education in France at Caen College and at the Lycee Henri IV in Paris. The Lycee specialised in science and mathematics. He then began an apprenticeship with Breguet et Fils of Paris, the foremost watch and clockmaker of France.

It was while he was at Breguet that his father's various enterprises foundered, largely as a result of too much invention and not enough attention to business matters. Marc and Sophia were arrested in 1821 and interned in the King's Bench debtors' prison, Southwark. By August 1821 Marc's influential friends, who included the Duke of

Isambard Kingdom Brunel working at his desk.

Wellington, succeeded in getting overdue money out of the Treasury to pay off his debts. This was moneys owed to Marc for Government contracts. Marc and Sophia returned home and in August 1822 the sixteen year old Isambard came back from France to work in his father's office.

At this point we might usefully compare the life experiences of Robert and Isambard. We know that they will meet and become friends. At age sixteen Robert, who had hardly known his mother, had been brought up by his father in a rough Northumbrian mining community. His education was sketchy, he had been a coal pit apprentice at the same age that Isambard had emerged from a comprehensive science based education in France to experience the rarefied company of notable scientists of the day. As a result, I K Brunel did not exhibit the single minded loyalty to the steam locomotive that Robert had imbibed while at his father's side.

For instance, Isambard and his father wasted ten years and £15,000 of Marc's money trying to develop the 'GAZ' engine, which was based on the theories of Davy and Faraday. Some time later Isambard again wasted much time and money on another rival to the steam engine, Clegg and Samuda's atmospheric railway system of 1838. Despite these aberrations, I.K Brunel's inclusion in this bookazine is appropriate due to the perfection of his railway engineering and also to mark his enterprise and courage in the building of ocean going ships driven by huge steam engines of his design.

In 1825 the Brunels began their great battle to drive a tunnel beneath the Thames from Rotherhithe to Wapping. Marc had invented and patented a rectangular tunnelling shield with thirty-six work places for the miners. The shield was pushed against the tunnel face by screws acting against the brickwork behind it. A brick width of earth was shovelled away, the frame was levered forward, and a new brick course was put in behind it. By this means the frame would move forward about a foot each day.

There had been two earlier attempts to tunnel under the Thames, Marc's shield was designed to cope with the unstable subsoil that had ruined those initial forays. However, it was soon clear that the conditions of the subsoil were even worse than had been allowed for. Despite this, by 1827 350 feet of tunnel had been completed, then Marc fell ill, his resident engineer resigned and Isambard was appointed in his place. At the age of twenty-one he displayed great courage and energy. On one occasion he

Plans for Isambard Kingdom Brunel's tunnel under the River Thames, London.

The Thames Tunnel after
inundation by water.

spent five continuous days underground, sleeping when he could on the planking erected for spoil collection. When the tunnel roof gave way he had himself lowered in a diving bell suspended from a boat so as to find the weak point in the river bed. When the tunnel flooded again, he and three others rowed themselves to the site of the break in the flooded tunnel to examine the bank of mud that had poured through the shield.

He was badly injured by a heavy fall through a manhole in the works yard in October, but still took his place at a banquet held in the completed section of the tunnel a month later. The next year he was nearly drowned when water again broke in while he was underground, the ill effects from which kept him away for several months. In 1828, due to the financial difficulties of the tunnel company, work on the tunnel ceased and the face was bricked up. The tunnel was not to be finally completed until 1843.

Part of Isambard's convalescence had been spent in Bristol at Clifton. When he learned of a competition to design a bridge that could span the Avon gorge he submitted four out of the twenty-two entries for consideration. Eventually, in 1831, his design for a suspension bridge was accepted. Work started in August that year, but riots in Bristol prevented progress which, together with some financial difficulties, meant the bridge was not completed until 1864. However, in 1836, while the stonework was being constructed, a one inch bar was drawn across the Avon gorge between the two towers. The bar was installed to enable material to be transported from

People in the Thames Tunnel.

one side of the gorge to the other, but a fault developed. Isambard, then thirty years of age, rectified the problem while suspended over the 230 foot drop in a basket.

In 1829, when his near contemporary, Robert Stephenson, was fully occupied with the production of steam locomotives for the Liverpool and Manchester Railway and many other young engineers were making names for themselves, Isambard felt himself to be in the doldrums. He had tried for the post of engineer to the

Newcastle and Carlisle Railway and again as engineer to the Birmingham and Bristol Railway. He had well connected friends and had himself been elected a member of the Royal Society in 1830, but still he lacked an appointment that would establish his credentials.

However, in 1833 his fortunes began to improve. The merchants of Bristol had decided that they needed a railway to connect their port to London in order to compete with the rival port of Liverpool. Initially they were unable

The partially-built structure of the Clifton Suspension Bridge, spanning the Avon Gorge in Bristol.

The Clifton Suspension Bridge in Bristol was completed a few years after Brunel's death.

The Clifton Suspension
Bridge in all it's glory.

A GWR 4-2-2 broad gauge locomotive at Swindon Station in Wiltshire.

to attract sufficient financial backing, but gained further support in 1832 and by 1833 were in a position to look for an engineer. Charles Babbage recommended Isambard, who was duly appointed. The Great West Road and the stage coaches that travelled on it had a new rival, The Great Western Railway Company.

Isambard began his survey of the line, spending many hours out of the twenty-four at the task. In 1834 he gave evidence before the House of Commons Committee for eleven days. The Royal assent for the full line was granted in 1835, and he began to set out the 117 mile route, avoiding gradients and severe curves that might limit the speed of trains travelling over his new railway.

George Stephenson's 4 foot 8 1/2 inch track gauge had been rejected by Isambard in favour of a broad 7 foot gauge that would allow lower centres of gravity, wider fireboxes and larger cylinders to be built into the locomotives that would haul the trains. It is doubtful that any of Stephenson's ideas could have been uncritically accepted by this young engineer, who had listened from childhood to the table talk of men of science like his father's friend, Sir Humphry Davy.

In receipt of a £2,000 annual salary, Isambard was able to set up a rather grand house at 18 Duke Street, overlooking St James' Park. The following year he married Mary Horsley whom he had known since 1832.

In less than six years, the line to Bristol was opened throughout its whole length. It had been divided into nine sections and the work had proceeded from both ends. Not only had Isambard rejected Stephenson's gauge but he also rejected the length of the rails, the shape of the rails and the way they were supported. Three foot five inch rail lengths, held by chairs on stone blocks had been suitable for the Liverpool and Manchester. The GWR was laid with fifteen foot bridge rails fixed directly to longitudinal timbers having cross members and piles at fifteen foot centres. This proved to be a mistake. Though the ride was firm and the rails minimally stressed, it was difficult to prevent settlement of the timbers between the piles. Soon the first twenty-two miles of the track had to be altered to prevent the piles from propping up the timber-borne rail ends, which then imparted a 'see-sawing' motion to the trains.

At this stage, Brunel almost lost the confidence of some of the Great Western Railway board of directors. The Liverpool contingent was of the opinion that Brunel should seek the advice of the Stephensons. As we have seen, Brunel's locomotives were inadequate for their task, and in 1840 Daniel Gooch had been given a free hand to produce his own designs.

Nevertheless, the railway that Brunel went on to create was magnificently proportioned, endowed as it was with impressive earthworks, viaducts and elegant bridges. The

A man operating a junction signal post on the Great Western Railway.

stations at Bristol Temple Meads and Bath had Tudor style hammer beam detail that enhanced the beauty of an unbuttressed over all roof. The second Paddington Station

Brunel's Elizabethan hammer beam roof and colonnade at the Great Western Railway Station, Bristol Temple Meads.

replaced the temporary building of 1838, and was built in 1854 and included the Great Western (Royal) Hotel. In this case, Isambard's station roof was after Joseph Paxton's design for the Crystal Palace built for the Great Exhibition of 1851. The hotel, by P C Hardwick, was in the style of a French chateau.

At Box Hill, which stood in the way of the line six miles west of Chippenham, Isambard excavated a 9,600 foot tunnel on a falling gradient of one in a hundred towards its western end. Eight shafts were sunk to enable digging to proceed, the maximum depth was about 300 feet. The strata that lay within the hill had been checked by sinking smaller 'test' shafts. The tunnelling began in 1838 but the work was sometimes halted by flooding, however the line generally advanced by about six feet per day. A thousand men worked in shifts around the clock, though

a hundred of these would lose their lives before the tunnel was completed in 1841. The face of the excavation was thirty-six feet high and thirty feet wide, and the tunnel was left unlined where it passed through hard rock. A ton of gunpowder was used every week to blast through the rock face. And this was only the first of the eight tunnels that he had to build between Chippenham and Bristol.

One of the most notable aspects of Isambard's personality was his ability to direct his energies to more than one project. Far from being content at his sudden change of fortune in 1835, when at one moment he despaired of ever making a name for himself, then at the next he was appointed engineer in charge of the Great Western Railway, he subsequently set himself an even greater challenge by proposing to continue his transport system across the Atlantic to the shores of America. As a

The western entrance to Box Tunnel.

The Great Western Steamship, designed by Isambard Kingdom Brunel, passing Portishead on her first voyage from Bristol to New York.

result of this proposal, made at a GWR meeting in August 1835, the 205 foot keel of the longest ship in the world was laid at a Bristol shipyard the following June.

The Great Western paddle steamer was Isambard's concept of a link between nations, where passengers could travel via the Great Western Railway from London to Bristol, and from there to the USA by the company's steamship. Despite the ongoing problems at Box Tunnel,

Isambard applied himself to the design of the massive pair of steam engines that would drive the twin paddles of the SS Great Western. It was to be the biggest marine engine that had ever been built, though its working pressure was only 5 lbs per square inch. Brunel was assisted by the expertise of Captain Claxton, a retired naval officer, and T P Guppy, the Bristol Railway director, who were both members of the building committee. By July 1837 she was

launched, and in April 1838 made the passage to New York in eighteen days, returning in fourteen days. The 500 ton American sailing ships which had dominated the Atlantic trade now had a speedier rival. SS Great Western. carried on to make sixty-seven crossings in eight years, and was eventually broken up in 1857 after twenty years of service.

The simultaneous conjunction of his enterprises continued. In July 1839 he began the construction of his second ship the SS Great Britain, a 3,500 ton iron hulled steamer with screw propulsion. Its 15,000 horsepower engines, designed by Isambard, were arranged to drive a propeller shaft longitudinally. Four cylinders in pairs at 60° drove an over head crankshaft with an eighteen foot wheel that was partially visible within a skylighted housing above deck. Toothed chains around the great wheel rotated a smaller wheel on the propeller shaft. This ship

The SS Great Britain,
moored in Bristol.

was completed in July 1843. The merchants of Bristol had good reason to be delighted by the energy of their young engineering genius. Not only had he connected them with London, but concurrently provided a potentially rapid connection with New York and created plenty of jobs for the workmen of their city. Unfortunately for Bristol, however, the dock company failed to enlarge its locks as they had promised, and once launched the ship had to be based at the rival port of Liverpool. Brunel's third ship, the Great Eastern, would be built in London. In the meantime, Brunel had an idea which he thought would speed up trains over the hilly terrain in South Devon.

Around the time that Isambard's Great Britain was being fitted out, he was trying to solve the problem of how to run a fast train service over the undulating route that had been chosen between Exeter to Plymouth. The line from Bristol to Exeter had been completed in 1844 and there were now 194 miles of track over which Daniel Gooch's Firefly engines made good speed from London. However, between Newton Abbott and Plymouth gradient of between 1 in 41 and 1 in 64 existed in at least ten places. Brunel judged that locomotive-hauled trains would be badly affected. He became interested in an idea patented by

Messrs Clegg and Samuda and demonstrated in 1840 on a short length of track at Wormwood Scrubs. It was known as the atmospheric system, and it did away with the need for a locomotive.

A cast iron pipe with a continuous slot in the top was laid between the tracks. The slot was made airtight by a greased leather flap. Stationary steam engines were erected at intervals along the line to pump air out of the pipe thereby creating a vacuum. The leading vehicle of the train was fixed to a piston within the pipe, and a linking arm slid in the slot, lifting the flap. Atmospheric pressure entered the pipe behind the piston and exerted up to a ton of force which propelled the train.

This system, which was also used on the London to Croydon line, had been rejected by the Stephensons. George said that it was little better than using rope haulage. Isambard, however, saw that light trains could be run at high speeds over gradients that caused trouble for steam locomotives. He recommended that the South Devon Railway should be a single line, atmospheric system. By September 1847, fifteen miles between Exeter and Teignmouth became operational, and in January 1848 the service reached Newton Abbot. However, despite the

The atmospheric system installed in Dawlish, Devon.

fact that an amazing 68 miles per hour had been recorded with a 28 ton train, the atmospheric experiment was discontinued later the same year.

It had been an expensive and embarrassing mistake which had cost the South Devon's shareholders several hundreds of thousands of pounds. Brunel himself had invested, and lost, his own money. Expensive Italianate pumping houses had been constructed with good quality steam pumping engines within them. Fuel costs had been high, and the constant attention to the continuous leather flap that was required in order to maintain an airtight seal had not been foreseen. After September 1848 the line was worked throughout by steam locomotives.

London was finally connected to Plymouth in April 1849, and the 249 mile journey which once took several days by stage coach could now be done in seven hours. In order to take the line over the slopes of Dartmoor, Isambard built a number of cheap timber viaducts of impressive height. His viaduct at Ivybridge had eleven 60 foot spans with a maximum height of 104 feet. The piers were of masonry and were quite slender. These timber bridges and viaducts were cleverly designed and carefully pre-tested to discover the loading limits of yellow pine. The most graceful of his bridges was probably the one built across the Thames at Maidenhead, where semi elliptical arches of brick span a distance of 128 feet, very large for brickwork and much criticised at the time for being

A cut-away example of the atmospheric railway.

The Royal Albert Bridge under construction.

'unsafe'. This bridge still serves the line today, now carrying far heavier trains than were originally anticipated.

Perhaps his most impressive bridge was the Royal Albert at Saltash. A bridge had to be provided over the Tamar River about three miles west of Plymouth in order to connect Plymouth with Penzance for the Cornwall Railway Company. Navigational requirements stipulated a hundred feet of mast room at high tide. The river at this point is just over a thousand feet wide. To keep the costs down, Brunel designed a single track bridge with an overall length of 2,200 feet. It had two main spans of 455 feet each and one central pier. Seventeen approach spans rest on masonry piers.

In 1853 work began on the central pier, the depth of water at high tide could be almost seventy feet. To create a 90 foot column of masonry Brunel floated an iron cylinder, which had been put together on the river bank, to the correct position before lowering it vertically onto the river bed. It took three and a half years to build the masonry foundations within the cylinder.

The two main spans, which weighed 1,000 tons each, were also constructed on the shore and tested under load. The first span was floated on pontoons into place between the piers in September 1857. Isambard directed operations from a platform erected in the centre of a truss, rather like a ship's bridge. It was to be a two hour session of

intense concentration that probably reminded him of the
occasion when, some years before, he had been at Robert
Stephenson's side during the building of the Britannia
Bridge. The span settled into position, a perfect fit, and was
slowly lifted by three foot increments until in July 1858 it
was at its design height, 100 feet above the river at high
tide. The second span was put in place under the directions
of his assistant

R P Brererton in July 1858. By then Isambard was a
sick man and spent months abroad convalescing. He no
longer signed the half yearly reports after August 1857.
When the Royal Albert Bridge was formally opened
by the Prince Consort in May 1859, Isambard was not
present. Later that year, a terminally ill Brunel lay on a
couch in a wagon while a special train hauled him across
the bridge that had been so difficult to complete.

The newly completed Royal
Albert Bridge

His final creation, the steamship Great Eastern, had been conceived while Isambard was in the early stages of designing this famous bridge. In fact, in 1853, when the central pier's foundations were under construction, tenders were being invited for the construction of the giant ship, which was to weigh almost 19,000 tons. The Eastern Steam Navigation Company, which was after the contract to convey mail to the far east, had accepted Isambard's design for a ship which he claimed would carry enough coal (10,000 tons) to make the return journey without refuelling. It would be three times the size of the Great Britain.

Shipbuilder John Scott Russell's tender had been accepted and his yard was on the north bank of the Thames at Millwall, Isle of Dogs. Unable to afford to make a dock of the size required, Russell's solution was to construct the hull parallel to the river bank 300 feet from the low water mark. This meant that the ship would have to be launched sideways. The 692 foot long hull was made from 30,000 one inch plates, 10 feet by 2 feet 9 inches, which formed a double skin 2 feet 10 inches apart. To drive her through the water, Russell was to build the two great paddle wheels 53 feet in diameter, and the engines that would drive them. James Watt and Co. were contracted to build the engines that drove a 24 foot screw.

After four years of work on the muddy river bank, a launching date was set for the 3rd November 1857 (the first span of the Royal Albert Bridge at Tamar had just been put into place). In order to encourage the 12,000 ton hull to slide into the river without 'sticking', Isambard decided to install iron plates sliding on rails at a gradient of one in twelve resting on a timber and

Construction gets under way of the Great Eastern.

From left to right:
Engineers John Scott Russell, Henry Wakefield, designer Isambard Kingdom Brunel and Lord Derby at the first launching ceremony of the Great Eastern ship.

concrete platform. A great crowd gathered to watch. The steam winches on barges in the river pulled mightily and hydraulic rams were applied to the hull on the landward side. Despite two attempts the ship hardly budged and the crowd went home, disappointed.

A further attempt was made on the 30th November, when the ship moved thirty-three feet – and stuck again. Public interest was intense, and Isambard received advice from all and sundry. His friend, Robert Stephenson, provided moral support and some good advice as he attended the scene despite his own failing health. At last, on 31st January 1858, the Great Eastern was floated at high tide. No sooner was one problem solved than another arose, as the Eastern Steam Navigation Co. ran out of money. Scott Russell had been bankrupted, Brunel was working without salary – he had lost his investment too. The Great Ship Company was formed to complete the vessel. Isambard was now seriously ill and often abroad in search of healthier climes. He was unable to attend a banquet held after the engines were tested in the summer of 1859. He made his final visit to the ship on 2nd September, the day before she was due to make her maiden voyage to Holyhead. The photograph to which I refer at the opening of this chapter was taken that day. He stood unsupported for the picture to be taken, but soon collapsed and was rushed home to his sick bed at Great Duke Street.

On 8th September, while the Great Eastern was in the English Channel, one of the ship's funnels exploded. The huge water heater within it had become over pressured. Five stokers were killed and several others seriously injured. The terrible news reached Isambard on 10th September, and he died five days later. He was in his fifty-third year.

Isambard's life had been devoted to the advancement of a new means of transport that forever altered the way we regulate our clocks and our working lives. His fame does not result from the advancement of the steam locomotive, the locomotive designs that he had specified for the new Great Western Railway in 1836 had poor reputations and short lives. It was the young engineer, Daniel Gooch, who had learned his trade at Robert Stephenson's side who eventually provided the Great Western with efficient locomotives largely based on Stephenson's North Star 2-2-2. However, as the creator of the feat that was the Great Western Railway, and the magnificent steamships which transformed the navigation of the sea, I K Brunel is truly the engineer hero of British Steam.

The Great Eastern sets sail with the Atlantic telegraph cable on board. She is flying British and American flags.

The steamship Great Eastern, constructed under the direction of Isambard Kingdom Brunel.

A crowd of people gathers at the revolutionary ship SS Great Eastern designed and built by engineer Isambard Kingdom Brunel as she sits at her dock in New York City.